KAI THE KOALA POO

loves to eat! No matter the time of day, he is always ready for a snack. His favourite foods are ice cream and leaves.

FREDDIE THE FLAMINGO POO

is fabulous in every way. He loves throwing parties for all his poo friends and always arrives in style.

JOEY THE ROO POO

loves to hop! See if you can spot this extra special poo in one of the scenes.

TREETOP ADVENTURE

The poos are exploring the adventure playground. Georgie is looking for the sandpit and Freddie wants a go on the see-saw. Can you spot each of the poos having fun on their day out?

WHERE'S THE
ANIMAL POO?

ORCHARD

ORCHARD BOOKS

First published in Great Britain in 2020

by The Watts Publishing Group

1 3 5 7 9 10 8 6 4 2

© 2020 The Watts Publishing Group Limited

Illustrations by Dynamo Limited

Additional images © Shutterstock

A CIP catalogue record for this book is available from the British Library

ISBN 978 1 40836 300 3

Printed and bound in China

Orchard Books
An imprint of Hachette Children's Group
Part of The Watts Publishing Group Limited
Carmelite House
50 Victoria Embankment
London EC4Y 0DZ

An Hachette UK Company
www.hachette.co.uk
www.hachettechildrens.co.uk

WHERE'S THE ANIMAL POO?

MEET THE POOS

Look out, these wild animal poos are on the loose! They're having fun at the adventure playground, visiting an aquarium, and exploring some famous sights around the world.

Can you spot each of the poos in every scene?

GEORGIE THE GIRAFFE POO

is the leader of the group. She loves to explore with her friends and try new and exciting experiences.

SAFI THE SLOTH POO

likes to take things slowly. Nothing makes her happier than a lazy day hanging out with her poo friends.

POPPY THE PANDA POO

is the cheekiest of all the animal poos. She loves to joke around and prank her friends.

SCRUMPTIOUS SWEETS

The poos can't believe their luck! They're allowed to try lots of yummy treats in the sweet factory.

AXOLOTLS EVERYWHERE

The poos are surrounded by axolotls. Can you find all the friends among the mayhem?

ODD ONE OUT!

Spot the axolotl that looks different to the rest.

ICE, ICE, MAYBE?

It's hot outside so the animal poos are cooling off with a yummy ice cream. Anyone for sprinkles?

POOS TO THE RESCUE!

The animal poos are on a tour around the fire station. Who wants to have a go with the hose?

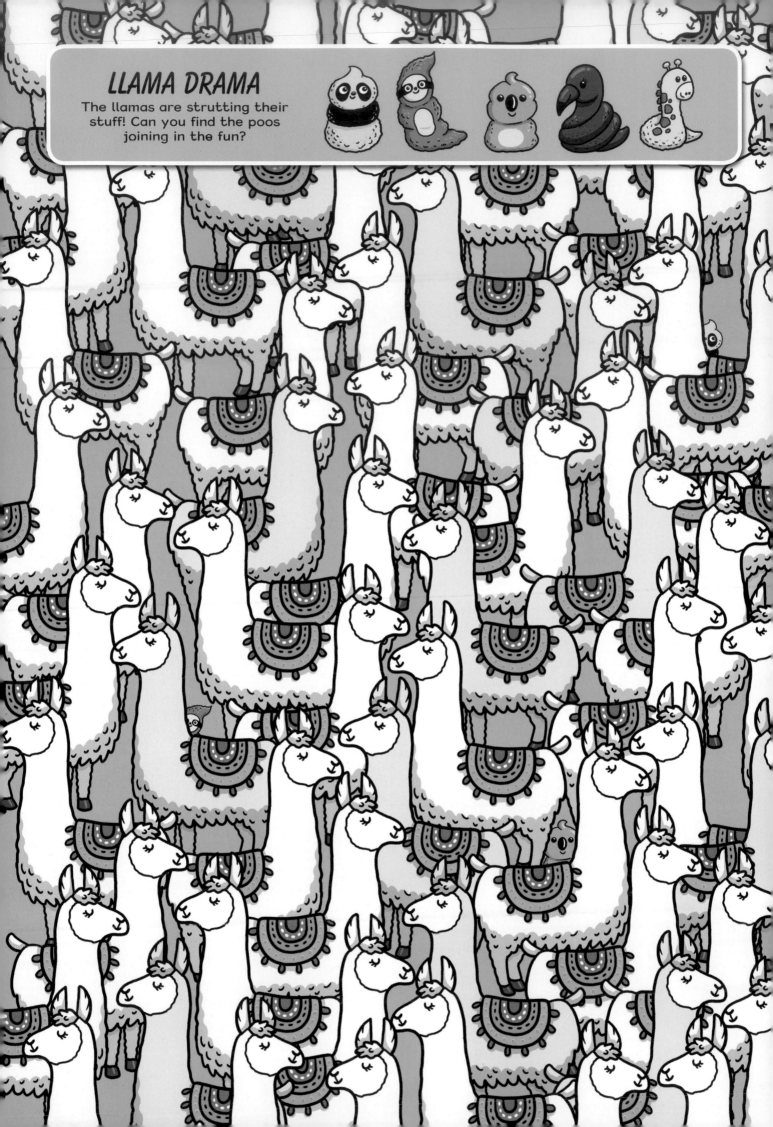

LLAMA DRAMA

The llamas are strutting their stuff! Can you find the poos joining in the fun?

ODD ONE OUT!

Which llama looks different to the others?

THE GREAT WALL

The poos are enjoying all the sights in China. Poppy is speeding along the Great Wall but . . . Safi . . . is . . . taking . . . her . . . time.

THE BIG BLUE

It's crowded with sea creatures here at the aquarium. Can you spot the poos amongst their underwater friends? Watch out for sharks!

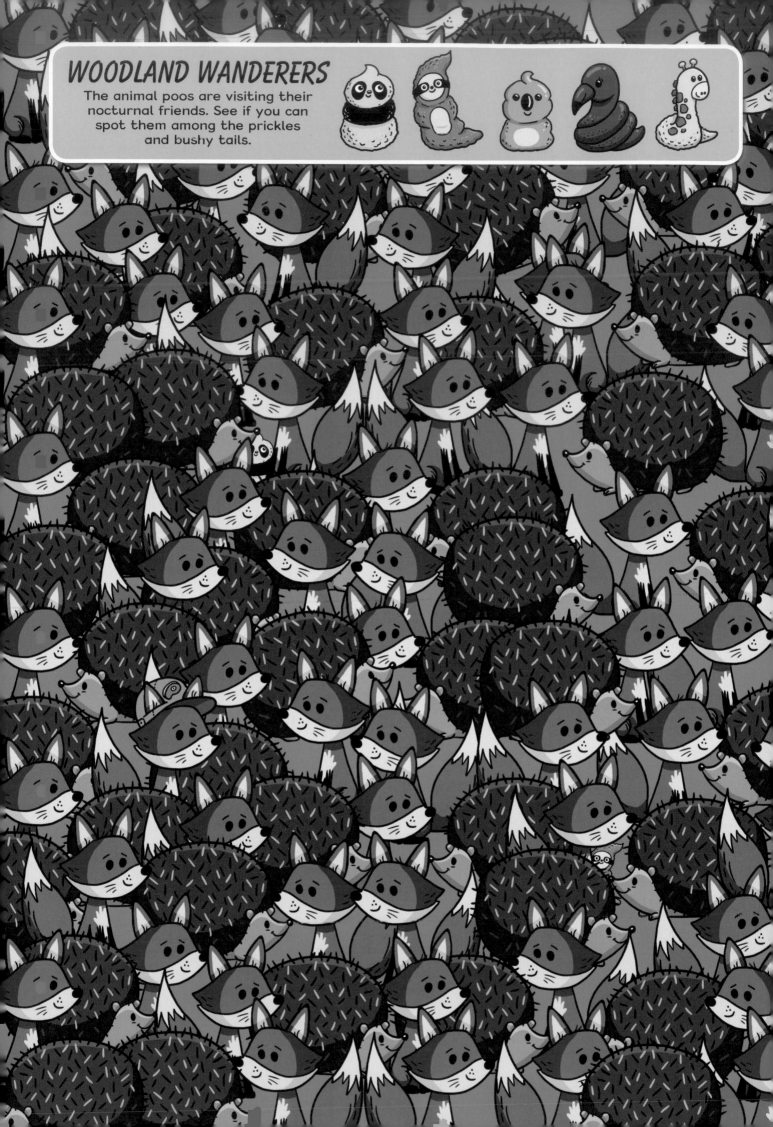

WOODLAND WANDERERS

The animal poos are visiting their nocturnal friends. See if you can spot them among the prickles and bushy tails.

ODD ONE OUT!

One fox and one hedgehog look different to the rest. Can you spot them?

DOWN UNDER

The animal poos are having a special day out in sunny Sydney. Can you spot them all?

GET YOUR SKATES ON

The poos are having lots of fun at the roller disco. Who can stay on their wheels the longest?

PENGUIN PALS

Can you find the poos hiding in this waddle of penguins?

ODD ONE OUT!

One of the penguins looks different to the others. Can you spot which one?

LET'S GO WILD

Georgie is showing the poos her friends from the savannah. Can you spot them all amongst the wildlife?

CLASSROOM CHAOS

There's a funny smell in the classroom . . . turns out the animal poos love to learn too! Can you find them?

ANSWERS

Hooray! You found all the animal poos. Now try to find all the extra items hidden in each scene.

TREETOP ADVENTURE

Twenty butterflies ☐

Two bees ☐

Three ice creams ☐

A girl hula hooping ☐

A bird eating chips ☐

Three dogs ☐

Two children squabbling ☐

One yellow truck ☐

Two children picking their noses ☐

One frog ☐

SCRUMPTIOUS SWEETS

Thirty six candy canes ☐

Seventeen cardboard boxes ☐

A yellow duck ☐

Two fried eggs ☐

Two gumball machines ☐

Seven children eating chocolate ☐

Three round green lollies ☐

Four sweet scoops ☐

A giant purple lolly ☐

A man in a purple coat ☐

AXOLOTLS EVERYWHERE

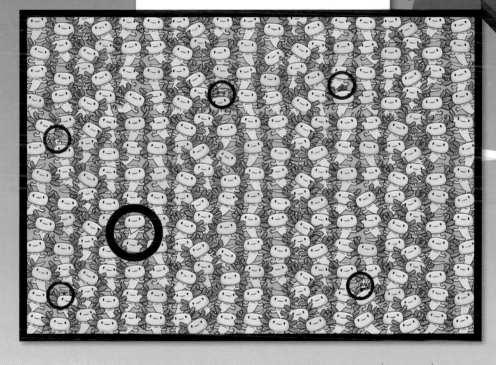

ICE, ICE, MAYBE?

Four pink doughnuts ☐

Five banana splits ☐

Two mice carrying ice cream cones ☐

Two crying children ☐

Eight napkin dispensers ☐

Four customers holding red spoons ☐

Two servers carrying trays ☐

Thirteen table menus ☐

Two green bins ☐

A boy standing on a stool ☐

POOS TO THE RESCUE!

- Eight mugs of tea ☐
- Four sandwiches ☐
- Two spanners ☐
- Two cats ☐
- Ten fire extinguishers ☐
- Eight spare tyres ☐
- Six ladders ☐
- Four spotty dogs ☐
- Eight clipboards ☐
- Three red hats ☐

LLAMA DRAMA

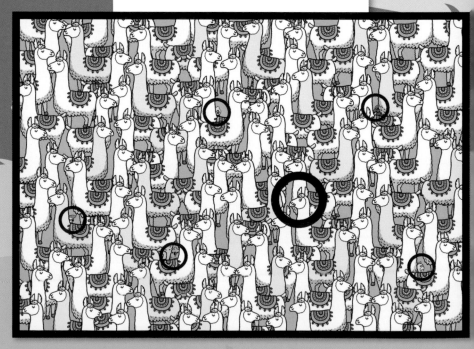

THE GREAT WALL

Eight men with beards ☐

A white rabbit ☐

Nine cranes ☐

Three umbrellas ☐

One purple flag ☐

Seven red lanterns ☐

Eight fortune cookies ☐

Seven people wearing headphones ☐

Seventeen people wearing sunglasses ☐

One child eating an ice cream ☐

THE BIG BLUE

Five starfish ☐

A shark ☐

A blue jellyfish ☐

A boy wearing a dinosaur t-shirt ☐

An ice cream ☐

A group of ten yellow fish ☐

Two babies in pink prams ☐

An angler fish ☐

A sea snail ☐

Two pufferfish ☐

WOODLAND WANDERERS

DOWN UNDER

Seven orange fish ☐

Three surf boards ☐

Two people playing guitar ☐

A purple umbrella ☐

Nine pigeons ☐

Two boomerangs ☐

Three people fishing ☐

A person in a kangaroo costume ☐

Eight bottles of water ☐

A puppet ☐

GET YOUR SKATES ON

A man with purple hair ☐

Four people wearing polka dots ☐

Rainbow bunting ☐

A pink flag ☐

A vending machine ☐

Four t-shirts with stars ☐

Two ice creams ☐

Three blue hats ☐

A skater with stripy leggings ☐

A spectator with a green rucksack ☐

PENGUIN PALS

LET'S GO WILD

- Six monkeys ☐
- Eleven dragonflies ☐
- Six birds ☐
- Five lions ☐
- Six hyenas ☐
- Nine hippo calves ☐
- Five frogs ☐
- Ten trees ☐
- Six zebra ☐
- A pair of binoculars ☐

CLASSROOM CHAOS

- A globe ☐
- Six handprints ☐
- A mug of tea ☐
- Twelve pots of pens ☐
- Eight pencil erasers ☐
- Nine pencil cases ☐
- One pigeon ☐
- Three pieces of scrunched up paper ☐
- Six glue sticks ☐
- A girl holding a paint pot ☐